Esther Rebecca ...
May 1, 1914.

SO-AIL-624

PARSIFAL: A DRAMA BY WAGNER
RETOLD BY OLIVER HUCKEL

BOOKS BY DR. HUCKEL

THROUGH ENGLAND WITH TENNYSON
A pilgrimage to places associated with the great Laureate
(Profusely illustrated, cloth, $2.00 net)

MENTAL MEDICINE
Some practical suggestions for everyday health
(Cloth, $1.00 net)

SPIRITUAL SURGERY
Some pointed analogies between body and soul
(Cloth, 75 cents net)

THE MELODY OF GOD'S LOVE
A new interpretation of the Twenty-third Psalm
(Cloth, 75 cents net)

WAGNER'S MUSIC-DRAMAS
Retold in English verse

RIENZI	RHEINGOLD
FLYING DUTCHMAN	WALKÜRE
TANNHÄUSER	SIEGFRIED
LOHENGRIN	GÖTTERDÄMMERUNG
TRISTAN	PARSIFAL

DIE MEISTERSINGER VON NÜRNBERG

RICHARD WAGNER: THE MAN AND HIS WORK
(Each, cloth, 75 cents net. Limp leather, $1.25 net)

THOMAS Y. CROWELL COMPANY

Parsifal

A · MYSTICAL · DRAMA · BY · RICHARD
WAGNER · RETOLD · IN · THE · SPIRIT · OF
THE · BAYREUTH · INTERPRETATION · BY
Oliver · Huckel

Thomas Y. Crowell Company
PUBLISHERS · NEW YORK

Copyright, 1903, by T. Y. Crowell & Co.

Published September, 1903

Twenty-first Thousand

Composition and plates by D. B. Updike

To my Wife

**IN LOVING MEMORY
OF BAYREUTH DAYS**

D. H.

CONTENTS

LIST OF ILLUSTRATIONS

ILLUSTRATED BY FRANZ STASSEN

FOREWORD

HE Parsifal of Richard Wagner was not only the last and loftiest work of his genius, but it is also one of the few great dramas of modern times,—a drama which unfolds striking and impressive spiritual teachings. Indeed, Parsifal may be called Richard Wagner's great confession of faith. He takes the legend of the Holy Grail, and uses it to portray wonderfully and thrillingly the Christian truths of the beauty, the glory, and the inspiring power of the Lord's Supper, and the infinite meaning of the redeeming love of the Cross. He reveals in this drama by poetry and music, and with a marvellous breadth and depth of spiritual conception, this theme (in his own words): "The founder of the Christian religion was not wise: He was divine. To believe in Him is to imitate Him and to seek union with Him. . . . In consequence of His atoning death, everything which lives and breathes may know itself redeemed. . . . Only love rooted in sympathy and expressed in action to the point of a complete destruction of self-will, is Christian love." (Wagner's Letters, 1880, pages 270, 365, 339.)

The criticism has sometimes been made that the basic religious idea of Parsifal is Buddhistic rather than Christian; that it is taken directly from the philosophy of Schopenhauer, who was perhaps as nearly a Buddhist as was possible for an Occidental mind to be; that the dominat-

ing idea in Parsifal is compassion as the essence
of sanctity, and that Wagner has merely clothed
this fundamental Buddhistic idea with the ex-
ternals of Christian form and symbolism. This
criticism is ingenious. It may also suggest that
all great religions in their essence have much
which is akin. But no one who reads carefully
Wagner's own letters during the time that he
was brooding over his Parsifal can doubt that he
was trying in this drama to express in broadest
and deepest way the essentials of Christian
truth. Christianity has no need to go to Buddh-
ism to find such a fundamental conception as
that of an infinite compassion as a revelation
of God.

The legend of the Grail, as Wagner uses it, has
in it the usual accompaniments of mediæval
tradition, — something of paganism and magic.
But these pagan elements are only contrasts
to the purity and splendor of the simple Christian truth portrayed. The drama suggests the
early miracle and mystery plays of the Christian
Church; but more nearly, perhaps, it reminds
one of those great religious dramas, scenic and
musical, which were given at night at Eleusis,
near Athens, in the temple of the Mysteries, before the initiated ones among the Greeks in the
days of Pericles and Plato. Here at Bayreuth
the mystic drama is given before its thousands
of devout pilgrims and music-lovers who gather
to the little town as to a sacred spot from all
parts of the world, — from Russia, Italy, France,
England, and America, — and who enter into
the spirit of this noble drama and feast of music

as if it were a religious festival in a temple of divine mysteries.

The sources of Wagner's story deserve a few words. The legend of the Holy Grail took many forms during the Middle Ages. It was told in slightly varying way in the twelfth century by the French writers Robert de Borron and Chrestien de Troyes, and in the early thirteenth century by Wolfram von Eschenbach in the strong German speech of Thuringia. The substance of these legends was that the precious cup, used for the wine at the Last Supper, and also used to receive the Saviour's blood at the Cross, was forever after cherished as the Holy Grail. It was carried from the Holy Land by Joseph of Arimathea and taken first to Gaul and later to Spain to a special sanctuary among the mountains, which was named Monsalvat. Here it was to be cherished and guarded by a holy band of Knights of the Grail. The same legend appears in the chronicles of Sir Thomas Malory, but instead of Gaul, early Britain is the place to which the Grail is brought. Tennyson's "The Holy Grail" in his Idylls of the King largely follows Sir Thomas Malory's chronicles. The American artist Edwin A. Abbey in his masterly paintings of the Grail legend as portrayed on the walls of the Boston Public Library, also follows Malory. Wagner, however, uses the version of Wolfram von Eschenbach, modifying it and spiritualizing it to suit his purposes. The German artist Franz Stassen, from whom our illustrations are taken, has entered with perfect appreciation into Wagner's version of the noble legend.   **xiii**

The following rendering of the Parsifal is not a close translation of the text, but rather a transfusion of the spirit. It is possibly as nearly a translation as Fitzgerald's rendition of Omar Khayyám, or Macpherson's version of the poems of Ossian. It is what may be called a free rendering, aiming to give the spirit rather than the language of the original.

The mere translations of the words of Parsifal, as given in the English texts of H. and F. Corder and M. H. Glyn, do not adequately represent the full value of the drama. Those versions were under the necessity of a strictly literal translation, which was further hampered in order to make the English words fit the music, and the result was far from satisfactory. The literal translation also unfortunately over-emphasizes certain parts and phrases in the drama which are somewhat harsh, but which at Bayreuth become much modified and refined, and are, therefore, so represented in this version.

The present telling of the story will be found to use all that Wagner has given in the words, but with the addition here and there of interpretative phrases, suggested by the drama itself at Bayreuth. Its purpose is to give an interpretation, a cumulative impression, the spirit of the words, music, and mystic meaning, blended together into one story and picture. It is made after a very careful study of the German text of Wagner for essential meanings, and after an appreciative hearing of the great drama itself, on two occasions, at Bayreuth. We present it in the form in which such sacred legends seem to find their most natural English setting, — in the form made classic in Tennyson's Idylls of the King.

It may also be interesting to note that the present version was planned ten years ago on a first visit to Bayreuth. Critical work on the German text and in the literature of the Parsifal legends was done later during two years at the universities of Berlin and Oxford. But the actual work of this translation and interpretation was done in the summer of 1902 at Bayreuth, and in part at Nuremberg and Munich. It may also be stated that this version is issued with the kind permission of Messrs. Schott and Company of London, the owners of the copyright of Wagner's words and music.

The music of Parsifal has been so often described and analyzed in critical papers that it is not necessary here to speak of it in detail. This word, however, may be in place. The marvellous music at Bayreuth helped in every way in the interpretation of the drama. Every part and phase of the thought and movement were brought forth in the various musical motives, adding emphasis and beauty and intensity of feeling. Now the music would whisper of the wondrous grace of the holy sacrament, or of the sweet beauty of God's world, clothed in the radiance of Good Friday; now it would reveal the sorrows of the gentle Herzeleide, or the awful anguish of Amfortas, or the deep rumblings of Klingsor's black art, or the fascinating music of the flower-maidens. Often came the pure tones that told of the guileless One, or the strong chords of mighty faith, or the ebb and swell of mystic bells, or the glory of the sacred Spear. Now came the regal blasts for Parsifal, and often and through it all, the splendid music of the Grail itself. The music was like a fragrant atmosphere to the drama, softening and refining what was harsh, giving a needed stress here and there, and investing the whole story with a subtle and uplifting charm.

The drama of Parsifal teaches its own great lessons of life. Yet one or two suggestions of interpretation may not be amiss, for it is confessedly one of the most mystical of modern dramas. It may perchance be considered as representing the strife between paganism and Christianity in the early centuries of the Church, — the powers of magic and the hot passions of the human heart contending against the advancing power of Christian truth and the victorious might of Purity as portrayed in the guileless hero. Or it may be considered as representing in a mystic legend the spiritual history of Christ coming in later presence among the sons of men and imaged in the mystic Parsifal. Wagner mentions that this Scripture was often in his mind when writing Parsifal — "Hath not God made foolish the wisdom of this world? The foolishness of God is wiser than men; and the weakness of God is stronger than men." Or this, further, it may represent, in striking and inspiring way, — that the pure in heart shall win the victories in life; that the guileless are the valiant sons of God; that the heart that resists evil passion and is touched by pity for the world's woe is the heart that re-

xvi

incarnates the passionate purity of the Christ
and can reveal again the healing power, the
Holy Grail of God.

Those who desire to study further the mystical
and spiritual meanings will find much helpful
suggestion in such books as The Argument and
Mystery of Parsifal, by Charles T. Gatty, F. S. A.
(London); A Study of Parsifal, by Alfred Gur-
ney, M. A. (London); Parsifal, — the Finding
of Christ through Art, by A. R. Parsons (New
York); or My Musical Memories, by Rev. H. R.
Haweis (chapter on "Parsifal").

It may be some time before the real Parsifal as
given at Bayreuth is fully appreciated by the
English-speaking public, although shortly the
special conditions which have hitherto reserved
its production to Bayreuth alone will be re-
leased, and the great drama will be heard in
other musical centres. This version is intended
to be a vivid reminder of the drama to those
who have seen it at Bayreuth, and also to give
to those who have not seen it a fuller glimpse of
the majestic story than has hitherto been possible to find in English. The genius of Wagner
as a musician has so far overshadowed all else,
that his genius as a poet and as an exquisite
reteller of the old legends has not been fully
appreciated.

Galahad, as Tennyson portrays him, will always
hold the first place with English readers as the
ideal knight of the Holy Grail. The matchless
diction of Tennyson has given the less perfect
form of the legend a supreme charm and beauty.
But Wolfram von Eschenbach's Parsifal, as

spiritualized and humanized in Wagner's lyric drama, will be seen to be in fuller accord with the whole cycle and development of the Grail legends, and at the same time gives the nobler story. It is a consummate parable of the contending passions and the heavenly aspiration, the ineffable pity and the mystic glory, of the human heart. It portrays an intensely human and heroic life, imaginatively identified with that of the very Christ.

"However mediæval the language and symbolism of Parsifal may be," says a modern critic, "one cannot but acknowledge the simplicity and power of the story. Its spiritual significance is universal. Whatever more it may mean, we see clearly that the guileless knight is Purity, Kundry is the Wickedness of the world expressed in its most enticing form, and King Amfortas suffering with his open wound is Humanity. One cannot read the drama without a thrill, without a clutching at the heart, at its marvellous meaning, its uplifting and ennobling lessons."

O. H.

Baltimore, Maryland, January 7th, 1903.

PARSIFAL. PART I

THE COMING OF PARSIFAL

ITHIN a noble stretch of
mountain woods,
Primeval forest, deep and
dark and grand,
There rose a glorious cas-
tle towering high, —
And at its foot a smiling,
shimmering lake
Lay in the still lap of a verdant glade.
'T was daybreak, and the arrows of the dawn
Were shot in golden glory through the trees,
And from the castle came a trumpet blast
To waken life in all the slumbering host, —
Warriors and yeomen in the castle halls.

And at the trumpet Gurnemanz rose up, —
Ancient and faithful servant of the Grail, —
Who sleeping lay under a spreading oak,
And called aloud to two youths sleeping yet:
"Hey! ho! ye foresters, loving the woods,
Loving your sleep as well. Wake with the day!
Hear ye the trumpet! Come, let us thank God
That we have power to hear the call of life,
And power to answer as the duty calls!"
And up they started, knelt in prayer with him,
And offered unto God their morning praise.

Then Gurnemanz: "Up now, my gallant youths,
Prepare the royal bath, and wait the King! . . .
Behold, his litter now is coming forth,
I see the heralds coming on before. . . .
Hail, royal heralds! Hail and welcome both!
How fares my Lord Amfortas' health to-day?

3

I hope his early coming to the bath
Doth presage nothing worse. I fain had thought
The healing herb that Sir Gawain had found
With wisest skill and bravest deed might bring
Some quick and sure relief unto the King."

To whom the herald-knight did make reply:
"Thou knowest all of this dread secret
    wound,—
The shame, the sorrow, and the depth of it,
Its evil cause and the dark curse upon it,—
And yet forsooth thou seemest still to hope?...
The healing herb no soothing brought, nor
    peace.
All night the sleepless King has tossed in pain,
Longing for morning and the cooling bath."

Then Gurnemanz, downcast and saddened,
    said:
"Yea, it is useless, hoping thus to ease
The pain unless we use the one sure cure,—
Naught else avails although we search the
    world.
Only one healer and one healing thing
Can staunch the gaping wound and save the
    King."

And eagerly the herald asked: "What cure is
    this,
And who the healer that can save the King?"

But Gurnemanz quick answered: "See the
    bath
Is needing thee, for here doth come the King!"

4

But as he spake, e'er yet the King appeared,
Another herald, looking far away,
Beheld a woman coming, riding wild,
And quick exclaimed: "See there, a flying witch!
Ha! how the devil's mare is racing fast
With madly flying mane! Nearer she comes!...
'T is Kundry, wretched Kundry, mad old Kun-
dry—
Perhaps she brings us urgent news? Who
knows?
The mare is staggering with weariness,—
No wonder, for its flight was through the air,—
But now it nears the ground, and seems to
brush
The moss with sweeping mane. And now, look
ye!
The wild witch flings herself from off the mare
And rushes toward us!"

      And Kundry came,
Her dark eyes flashing wildly, piercing bright;
Her black hair loose; her rude garb looser still,
Yet partly bound with glittering skins of
snakes;
And panting, staggering ran to Gurnemanz,
And thrust into his hands a crystal flask
With the scant whisper, "Balsam—for the
King!"
And on his asking, "Whence this healing
balm?"
She answered: "Farther than thy thought can
guess.
For if this balsam fail, then Araby
Hath nothing further for the King's relief.
Ask me no further. I am weak and worn."

5

And now the litter of the King drew near,
Attended by a retinue of knights.
High on the couch the King Amfortas lay,
His pale face lined with suffering and care;
And looking toward the King, then Gurnemanz
Spake with his own sad heart: "He comes,
  my King,—
A helpless burden to his servitors.
Alas, alas! That these mine eyes should see
The sovereign of a strong and noble race,
Now in the very flower and prime of life,
Brought low, and made a bounden slave
Unto a shameful and a stubborn sickness!...
Ye servitors, be careful of this couch!
Careful! Set down the litter tenderly!
I hear the King, our Master, groan in pain."

Then they set down the couch, and soon the
  King,
Raising himself a little, spake to them:
"My loving thanks, sir knights. Rest here
  awhile.
How sweet this morning and these fragrant
  woods
To one who tossed the weary night in pain.
And this pure lake with all its freshening waves
Will lighten pain and brighten my dark woe.
Where is my dear Gawain?"

                    And one spake up:
"My Lord Gawain has hasted quick away.
For when the healing herb that he had brought
After such daring toils, did disappoint,
Then he set forth upon another quest."

Then said the King: "Without our word?
Alas that he should go on useless quests
And seem to do despite unto the Grail!
For it is ordered by divine command
That I should suffer for my grievous sin,
And naught can help me but one single thing.
O woe, if in his far-off quests for me
He is ensnared by Klingsor's hateful arts!
I pray you, sirs, venture no more for me, —
It only breaks my peace, and grieves my heart.
Naught will avail. I only wait for Him, —
'By pity 'lightened.' Was not this the word?"

And Gurnemanz: "So thou hast said to us."

And softly yet spake on the suffering King:
"'The guileless One.' Methinks I know him
     now!
His name is Death, for only Death can free
     me!"

Then Gurnemanz to ease the King's sad
     thoughts
Held forth the crystal flask with soothing
     words:
"Nay, nay, my King. Essay once more a cure, —
A balsam brought for thee from Araby."

And the King asked: "Whence came this bal-
     sam flask,
So strange in form, and who has brought it
     here?"

And Gurnemanz: "There lies the woman now!
The wild-eyed Kundry, weak and weary-worn,

7

As if the journey sapped her very life. . . .
Up, Kundry! Here's his majesty the King!"

But Kundry would not rise, or could not else.

Then spake the King: "O Kundry, restless,
strange,
Am I again thy debtor for such help?
Yet I will try thy balsam for my wound,
And for thy service take my grateful thanks."

But Kundry muttered: "Give no thanks to me.
What will it help, — or this, or e'en the bath?
And yet, away, I say! On to the bath!"
Then the King left her, lying on the ground,
And off he moved upon the couch of pain,
Longing to bathe him in the shining lake,
Hoping against all hope to ease his soul,
And quiet in his body the fierce pains.

And one spake up: "Why lies that woman
there, —
A foul and snarling thing on holy ground?
Methinks her healing balm is witching drug
To work a further poison in the King. . . .
She hates us! See her now! How hellishly
She looks at us with hot and spiteful eyes!
She is a heathen witch and sorceress!"

But Gurnemanz, who knew her well, replied:
"What harm has ever come to you from her?
And oft she serves us in the kindliest ways.
For when we want a messenger to send
To distant lands where warrior-knights in fight
Are serving God, she quick takes up the task;

8

Before you scarcely know is gone and back.
A marvel is her wondrous speed of flight.
Nor does she ask your help at any time,
Nor tire you with her presence, nor her words.
But in the hour of danger, she is near, —
Inspiring by her brave and fiery zeal,
Nor asking of you all one word of thanks.
Methinks a curse may still be on her life, —
She is so wild and strange, so sad her very eyes.
But now, whate'er the past, she is with us,
And serves us to atone for earlier guilt.
Perchance her work may shrive her of her sins.
Surely she does full well to serve us well,
And in the serving help herself and us."

Then spake again a knight: "Perchance her
    guilt
It was, that brought calamity on all our land."

But Gurnemanz: "My thought of her goes far
In memory to days and years long past.
And it was always when she was away
And we alone, that sudden mishap fell.
This I have seen through many, many years.
The aged King, our Titurel beloved,
He knew her well for many years beyond.
'T was he who found her sleeping in these woods,
All stiff and rigid, pale and seeming dead,
When he was building yonder castle-towers.
And so did I myself, in recent days,
Find her asleep and rigid in the woods, —
'T was when calamity on us had come
So evil and so shameful from our foe, —
That dread magician of the mountain heights.

9

Say, Kundry, wake and answer me this word?
Where hadst thou been in those dark evil
    days, —
At home, afar, awake or fast asleep, —
When our good King did lose the holy Spear?
Why were you not at hand to give us help?"

And Kundry muttered: "Never do I help!"
Then said a knight: "O brother Gurnemanz,
If she is now so true in serving us,
And if she does such strange and wondrous
    deeds,
Then send her for the missing holy Spear
For which the King and all the land are fain."

But Gurnemanz with gloomy looks replied:
"That were a quest beyond her, beyond all —
That lies within the guarded will of God.
O how my heart leaps up in memory
Of that blest symbol of the Saviour's power!
O wounding, healing, wonder-working Spear,
Companion of the Grail in grace divine,
A radiant shaft for consecrated hands.
What saw I? Hands unholy snatched thee up,
And sought to wield thee in unholy ways.
I see it all again, — that dark and fatal day
When our good King Amfortas, all too bold,
Forgetful of the evil in the world,
Went straying far out from the castle walls,
And loitered through the green and shady
    woods;
And there he met a woman passing fair,
With great eyes that bewitched him with their
    light,

And as he stayed and lost his heart to her,
He lost the Spear. For on a sudden came
Athwart them that foul-hearted, fallen knight,
The evil-minded Klingsor, and he snatched
The holy Spear and mocking rushed away.
Then broke an awful cry from the King's lips;
I heard and hurrying fought the evil knight,
As did the King, parrying blow on blow,
And at the last the King fell wounded sore
By that same Spear that once was holy health.
This is the fatal wound that burns his side,—
This wound it is that ne'er will close again."

And when the knights asked further of the deed
And what of Klingsor, the foul-hearted knight,
Then Gurnemanz sat down and told this tale, —
The four young knights ensconced around his
          feet, —
"Our holy Titurel knew Klingsor well.
For in the ancient days when savage foes
Distressed the kingdom with their heathen
          craft,
One mystic midnight came a messenger
Of God to Titurel, and gave to him
The Holy Grail, the vessel lustrous pure,
Wherein the crimson wine blushed rosy-red
At that Last Supper of the feast of love;
Wherein the later wine of His own blood
Was caught and cherished from the cruel Cross.
This gave the angel unto holy Titurel
And with it gave the radiant sacred Spear
That pierced the side and broke the suffering
          heart
Of Him, our heavenly Saviour on the Cross,

II

So that the water and the blood flowed forth
In mingled tide, — the sacrifice of love.
And for these precious witnesses of God
That told to men of saving health and power,
The holy Titurel did build an holy house, —
A sanctuary-stronghold on the heights
Of Monsalvat, forever given to God.
And ye, blest servants of the Holy Grail,
Ye know the sacred ways by which ye came
Into this holy service. Ye gave all
And purified your lives and hearts to God.
And with the consecration came the power,
By vision of the Grail, to do high deeds
And live the life of warriors of God.
This Klingsor came to holy Titurel
And asked to come into the company.
Long had he lived in yonder heathen vale
Alone, and shunned by all his kind.
I never knew what sin had stained his heart,
Or why he sought the castle of the Grail;
But holy Titurel discerned his heart
And saw the festering evil of his life,
And knew unholy purpose filled his soul
And steadfastly refused him at the gates.
Whereat in wrath the evil Klingsor swore
That if he could not serve the Holy Grail,
The Holy Grail should serve him by its power;
And he would seize it in his own right hand,
And some day be the master of them all.
Henceforth he waged a subtle, ceaseless war
Against Monsalvat and the holy knights.
He gave himself to dark and evil life
And learned the witchery of magic arts
To work the ruin of the Holy Grail.

Fair gardens he created by his art,
Through all the deserts, and therein he placed
Maidens of winsome witchery and power,
Who bloomed like flowers in beauty and in
  grace.
And in these subtle snares full many a knight
Was caught by magic wiles and lured and lost,
And no one knew where they had gone or why.
Then holy Titurel, grown old in years,
Gave up the kingdom to his only son,
The brave Amfortas. And by ceaseless quest
Amfortas learned the truth and waged fierce
  war
Against this Klingsor, evil to the heart,
Until at last in one unguarded moment,
As I have told you, e'en our noble King,
The good Amfortas, yielded to a sin, —
And lost the Spear, and had his fatal wound.
Now with the Spear within his evil grasp
Klingsor exults, and mockingly does tell
How his black fingers soon will hold the Grail."

Then the young knights who listened to the
  tale
Upstarted with the cry: "God give us grace
To wrest that sacred Spear from impious
  hands!"

But Gurnemanz thus checked them: "Listen
  yet!
Long did our King Amfortas kneel before
The sanctuary, praying in his pain
And seeking for a word of hope from God.
At length a radiance glowed around the Grail,

13

And from its glory shone a Sacred Face
That spake this oracle of mystic words:
> "By pity 'lightened,
>> My guileless One, —
>> Wait for him,
>>> Till My will is done!"

And as the knights repeated these weird
    words, —
There came wild cries and shouting from the
    lake:
"Shame! shame! alas, the shame to shoot the
    swan!"
And as they looked, a wild swan came in sight;
It floated feebly o'er the flurried lake
And strove to fly, but wounded fluttered down
And sank upon the lake-shore, and was dead.
And Gurnemanz cried out: "Who shot the
    swan?
The King had hailed it as a happy sign,
Whene'er a swan came near him in its flight.
For since the earliest ages has this bird
Meant hope and health and holiness to men. —
Who dared to do this dastard deed of shame?"

Then came a knight leading a guileless boy
And said: "This is the one who shot the swan, —
And here more arrows like the cruel shaft
That hides itself within the bleeding breast."

To whom spake Gurnemanz: "What mean'st
    thou, boy,
By such a cruel, shameless deed as this?"

14

But the boy answered: "Yea, it was my shot.
I shot the swan in flight when high in air."

Then Gurnemanz: "Shame to confess such
    deed!
Such sacrilege within these holy woods,
Where seems to dwell the perfect peace of God.
Were not the woodland creatures kind to
    thee,—
Did not the sweet birds sing their songs to thee,
When first thou camest to these leafy haunts?
And this poor swan, so mild and beautiful,—
How could thy heart determine on such deed?
It hovered o'er the lake in circling grace,
Seeking the dear companion of its love,—
For e'en the heart of bird doth know sweet
    love,—
And seeming to make sacred all the lake.
Didst thou not marvel at its queenly flight,
And feel a reverence in thine inmost soul?
What tempted thee to shoot the fatal shaft,
And slay the bird and grieve the loving King?...
See where the deadly arrow smote its breast!
Behold the snowy plumage splashed with
    blood!
The spreading pinions drooping helpless now,
And in its eye the agony of death!
Slain by thy cruel heart that knows no shame!
Dost thou not see how wicked is thy deed?"

Then was the young boy stricken with remorse,
And drew his hand across his moistened eyes,
As if new pity dawned within his soul;
Then quickly snatching up his strong arched
    bow,

15

He broke it, and his arrows flung away.
And clutching at his breast as if in pain
He stood a time in conscious agony, —
Deep feeling surging through his stricken
    heart;
And then he turned again to Gurnemanz
With the brave words: "I did not understand
What evil I was doing with my bow."

"Whence art thou?" Gurnemanz did ask of
    him;
And dazed he answered: "That I do not know."
"But who thy father?"—"That I do not know."
"Who sent thee here?"—"I do not know e'en
    that."
Then Gurnemanz: "Yet tell me but thy name."

And in a strange and dazed way he replied:
"Once I had many. Now, I do not know."
And Gurnemanz spake sharply, half in wrath,
"Thou knowest nothing. Such a guileless
    soul, —
So wisely foolish, and so foolish wise, —
A very child in heart, yet strangely strong,
Ne'er have I found, except in Kundry here. . . .
Come, brother-knights, lift up the stricken swan
And bear it on these branches to the lake;
Nor speak of this sad sorrow to the King
To further grieve his deep-afflicted heart.
Stricken the King and wounded to his death,
This omen he may dwell on to his hurt."

And back unto the King's bath went the
    knights,
While Gurnemanz spake further to the lad:

"Speak out thy heart to me. I am thy friend.
Surely thou knowest much that thou canst say."

Then spake the boy and told him of his life:
"I have a mother,—Heartsrue is she called.
And on the barren moorland is our home.
My bow and arrows have I made myself
To scare the eagles in the forest wilds."

Then Gurnemanz: "Yea, thou hast told me
     true,
For thou thyself art of the eagle brood.
I see a something kingly in thy look.
Yet better had thy mother taught thy hands
To spear and sword than this unmanly bow."

Whereat the wild witch Kundry raised herself
From where she lay along the bosky woods,
And hoarsely broke in: "Yea, his noble sire
Was Gamuret, in battle slain and lost
A month before his child had seen the light.
And so to save her son from such a death,
The lonely mother reared him in the woods,
And taught him nothing of the spear and sword,
But kept him ever as a guileless child."

Then spake the lad: "And once I saw a host
Of men pass by the borders of the wood,
A-glitter in the sun, and riding fast
On splendid creatures, prancing as they went.
Oh, I would fain have been like these fair men.
But, laughing gaily, on they galloped fast
And I ran after them to be like them,
And join the glittering host and see the world.

17

But though I ran, they faded from my sight.
Yet have I followed, over hill and dale.
Day after day I follow on their track,
And here I am as now you see me here.
My bow has done me service on the way
Against wild beasts and savage-seeming men."

And Kundry added: "Yea, the fiery boy
Has sent a terror into many hearts—
The wicked always fear the nobly good."
Then asked the boy in sweetest innocence:
"And who are wicked, tell me, and who good?"

And Kundry spake:"Thy mother, she was good.
She grieved for thee, but now she grieves no
    more.
For as I lately rode along that way
Coming with haste from far Arabia,
I saw her dying, and she spake to me,
And sent her blessing to her darling boy."

At which the boy with sudden childish rage:
"My mother dead! and sent a grace by thee,—
Thou liest, woman! Take thy false words back!"
And still impetuous and unreasoning,
Fighting the facts of life in rebel mood
(A child of sudden temper, guileless heart),
He seized her, struggling with a furious might
To make her unsay what her lips had told.
Perhaps he might have harmed her in his wrath,
Had not the agèd Gurnemanz come near,
And drawn him back, with the sharp-spoken
    words:
"Impetuous child, restrain thy violence!

18

This woman harms thee not. She speaks the
    truth!
Kundry has seen it, for she never lies."

And at the word, the lad grew calm again,
And silent stood with still and stony stare,
Until his heart broke out in woe afresh
(A guileless child, not knowing strong control),
And he was seized with trembling, and he
    swooned.

Then Kundry, bearing naught of hate or spite,
Ran to a pebbly brook that flowed near by,
And brought cold water in an ancient horn,
Sprinkled the lad, and gave him some to drink.

And Gurnemanz, with kindly look at her,
Spake out: "Thy deed is worthy of the Grail, —
A cup of water fails not of reward;
And sin is conquered by the deeds of good."

But Kundry muttered still: "I do no good!"
Then in still lower tone to her own self:
"I do no good, I only long for rest.
O weary me! Would I might never wake!
Yet dare I sleep? It means calamity
To those whom I in vain have tried to serve.
Resist I cannot! Yea, the time has come!
I feel the awful spell upon mine eyes, —
Slumber I must! Slave of that evil one
Who wields his black art from the mountain
    height.
Sleep, sleep, to sleep! I must! I must! I must!"
With this she crept away and laid her down
Within a thicket of the forest woods.

Meanwhile the litter of the King came back
With all its retinue of gallant knights.
And Gurnemanz held up the tottering lad,
Still sorrowing at the sad news come to him,
And slowly led him toward the castle gate,
While softly speaking to him graciously:
"See how our King Amfortas from the bath
Is carried by his loving servitors.
The sun is rising high. The time has come
When we shall celebrate our holy Feast.
There will I lead thee. If thy heart be pure,
The Grail will be to thee as food and drink."
Then asked the lad: "What is this thing, the
Grail?"

And Gurnemanz: "I may not tell thee that,
But if to serve it thou art surely called,
Then shalt thou know its meaning to the full.
Somehow I feel and hope that thou shalt know,
Else what has led thy footsteps to this height.
Yet no one sees the glory of the Grail
Save those to whom it shall reveal itself."

Then on they moved, and softly spake the lad:
"I scarcely move, and yet I seem to run, —
What is the meaning of this strange new
thing?"

And Gurnemanz made answer: "Here, my child,
There is no space and time, but all is one, —
For here we breathe the atmosphere of God, —
A boundless Here and an eternal Now."

Then on they went, and soon were lost to view
Within the gateway of a rocky cliff;

Sometimes came glimpses of them as they climbed
The sloping passages within the cliff—
A cloistered corridor of carven columns—
And paused a moment at some rocky window
To see the grandeur of the mountain heights.
The soft notes of a trumpet called them up,
And silver bells were chiming melodies.

At length they reached the noble pillared hall
Within the castle of the Holy Grail,
For here the sacred feast was always kept, —
And here were gathering the blessèd knights.
Clothed were they all in tunics of gray-blue, —
The color of the softened light of heaven, —
With mantles of pale scarlet, flowing free, —
The very tincture of the blood they served, —
And on the mantles snow-white soaring doves,
The symbol of the Holy Spirit's gift.
And with a solemn joy they took their place
Along the tables of communing love;
The while from the great vaulted dome above
Came ever-growing sound of chiming bells.

Then spellbound stood the lad and gazed around,
Amazed at all the glory of the hall,
And all the solemn splendor of the scene,
Till Gurnemanz stooped down and whispered low:
"Now give good heed, and if thy heart be pure,
And thou art called, then surely thou shalt know."

Then sang the knights this chorus soft and slow:
"O HOLY feast of blessing,
Our portion day by day;
In thee God's grace possessing,
That passeth not away.
Who doth the right and true,
Here findeth strength anew;
This cup his hand may lift,
And claim God's holiest gift."

And from the mid-height of the lofty dome
The voices of the younger knights replied:
"As anguished and holy
The dear Saviour lowly,
For us sinners His own life did offer;
So with hearts pure and free,
Forever do we
Our lives unto Him gladly proffer.
He died — our sins atoned for thus, —
He died — yet liveth still in us!"

And from the topmost of the glorious dome
A chorus of fresh boyish voices came:
"The faith doth live!
The Lord doth give
The Dove, His sacred token!
Drink at this board
The wine outpoured,
And eat the bread here broken!"

And as they sang their sweet antiphonies,
A long procession through the splendid hall
Wended slow way, and bearing in the King,
The suffering Amfortas in his pain,

22

Still lying listless on his royal couch.
Before him walked a company of boys
Clothed in pale blue, and bearing high aloft
A mystic shrine in cloth of deepest crimson,
To signify the royal blood beneath.
And others followed bearing silver flagons
With wine, and baskets of the finest bread.
Slowly the King was carried to a couch
Within the midst, high-raised and canopied,
And just before him, of a pure white stone,
Traced with faint figures of the passion-flower,
Stood the communion table where was placed
The sacred shrine, still covered, of the Grail.

And when the hymns were ended, and the
    knights
Had taken their set places at the board,
Then there was silence. And from far away,
As if from some deep cavern of a tomb,
Behind the couch where King Amfortas lay
The muffled voice of aged Titurel
Spake with long silences between the words:
"My son Amfortas, art thou at thy post? . . .
Wilt thou unveil the Grail and bid me live? . . .
Or must I die, denied the saving vision?"

And King Amfortas cried in desperate pain:
"O woe is me to bear the burning wound
That shames me in the office of the Grail!
O father, do thou take the sacred trust
And let thy holy hands reveal the Grail
Once more, and live! And let me quickly die!"

But answered him the aged Titurel:
"Nay, nay, too feeble I to serve again.

23

I live entombed with but a breath of life,
Saved by the remnant of the grace of God.
My strength all gone, but my poor yearning
      heart
Still eager for the vision of the Grail;
For this alone can bring me comfort now.
Thine is the office. O unveil the Grail!
For serving faithfully thou mayst atone
For all the grievous sin of thy sad life."

But quickly King Amfortas stopped the knights
Who went to do his bidding at the shrine:
"Nay, leave the Holy Cup still unrevealed!
God grant that none of you may ever know
The torment that this vision brings to me
Which brings to you all rapture and all joy.
Here do I stand in office, yet accurst, —
My heart of lust to guard God's holiest gift,
And plead in prayer from lips all stained with
      sin, —
Pleading for you who purer are than I!
O direst judgment from the God of grace!
My inmost soul doth long for His forgive-
      ness,
I yearn for sign of His compassion,
Yet cannot bear His mercy in the Grail. . . .
But now the hour is nigh! I seem to see
A ray of glory fall upon the Cup!
The veil is raised! The sacred stream that flows
Within the crystal, gloriously shines
With radiance heaven-born. But as it glows,
I feel the well-spring of the blood divine
Pouring in floods into my anguished heart.
And then the full tide of my sinful blood

24

Ebbs out in tumult wild through this deep
   wound
Here in my side. It leaps in bounds of pain,
Like torments of the lowest depths of hell, —
Through this deep wound. Like His own wound
   it is,
Thrust through with bitter stroke of that same
   Spear,
And in the self-same place from which His tears
Of burning blood wept over man's disgrace
In holiest pity and divinest love;
And now from me, the highest office holding
And charged with holiest trust of God's good
   grace, —
From me the hot, impassioned blood is surging,
Renewed again by that first awful sin.
Alas, no deep repentance e'er can save
A sinner dyed in sins so scarlet red.
Naught can avail, but only one sure thing,
The healing touch of that thrice-sacred Spear,
Held in the pure hand of the guileless One.
Have mercy, O have mercy, pitying God!
Take back my birthright in the sacred trust!
Take back my life and all I hold most dear!
But give me healing, and Thy tender love, —
And let me die, and come to Thee pure-hearted!"

And as he ended in an anguished sob,
The boys' sweet voices chanted from the dome:
     "By pity 'lightened,
        My guileless One, —
    Wait for him,
       Till My will is done!"

Then softly all the knights cried: "'Tis God's will
25

That thou shouldst wait in suffering, yet
    hope. . . .
Fulfil thy duty: and reveal the Grail!"

While deep the voice of agèd Titurel:
"Unveil the Grail! Sir knights, unveil the Grail!"

Then they took off the cloth all purple-red,
And slowly brought to light the golden shrine,
And from it took the antique crystal Cup,—
Forever cherished as the Holy Grail,—
And set it on the table near the King,
Who writhed in silent anguish on his couch.

Then agèd Titurel: "The blessing now!"

And King Amfortas bowed in silent prayer
Before the Cup, while an increasing gloom
Spread through the room, and from the lofty
    dome
The voices of the boys sang soft and low:

    "**T**AKE ye, and drink My blood,
        In vow no death can sever!
    Take ye, My body eat,
        In love to live forever!
    Remember ye My life and love,
        And raise your hearts to Me above!"

And as the verse was ended, came a ray
Of dazzling light upon the crystal Cup,
And filled it with a radiant purple glory.
And with it came a streaming splendor down
That flashed a lustrous beauty all around.
And King Amfortas, with a brightening face,

Upraised the Holy Grail, and gently waved
Its glory to all sides. And all did kneel,
And raised their eyes in joyous reverence
Toward that bright glory in the darkened room.

And once again the agèd Titurel's voice:
"O rapturous vision of the grace of God!"

Then King Amfortas placed the Cup again
Upon the altar-table of the shrine,
And it was covered with the crimson cloth.
And from the silver flagons of the wine
And from the baskets of the sacred bread,
New consecrated by the Grail's own light,
Each knight received his portion gratefully,
And all sat down to eat the feast divine.
Then Gurnemanz did beckon to the lad
To come and eat. But he was all amazed,
And silent stood, nor heeded the kind word.

While from the height, boys' voices came again:
"WINE and bread of consecration,
    Once the Lord for our salvation
Changed for love and pity's sake
To the blood which He did shed,
To the body which He brake."

And answering them, the younger knights re-
    plied
In sweet antiphony amid the feast:
    "Blood and body, gift of blessing,
    Now He gives for your refreshing,
    Changes by His spirit true
    To the wine for you outpoured,
    To the bread that strengthens you."

27

And still in answer did the knights respond,
One group in joyous answer to the other:

"TAKE ye the bread,
    Change it again,
Your powers of life inspiring;
    Do as He said,
    Quit you like men,
To work out the Lord's desiring.

"Take of the wine,
    Change it anew
To life's impetuous torrent;
    This be the sign,
    Faithful and true,—
To fight as duty shall warrant!"

Then all the knights, with rapture in their
        hearts,
Rose joyfully and clasped each other's hands
And gave each other the blest kiss of peace,
And from their lips and from the dome's great
        height,
And from the younger knights the chorus
        broke:
            "Blessèd believing!
            Blessèd the loving!
            Blessèd the loving!
            Blessèd believing!"

But King Amfortas bowed his anguished head,
And held his wound all broken out afresh.
Slowly they carried him from out the hall
And slowly marched the knights with solemn
        joy,
Bearing the Grail within the covered shrine,

28

While bells were chiming in the lofty dome.
And then the lad—for he was Parsifal—
Tight clutched his heart in sorrowful distress
As King Amfortas groaned in bitter woe.
He stood in utter anguish overcome,
Breathing impulsive with deep sympathy,
But spake no single word, nor gave one sign
That he had understood the solemn feast,
Or seen the glory of the Holy Grail.
And when the last knight left the festal hall
And all the doors were closed, then Gurnemanz
Came to the lad and shook him from the spell
And asked: "What sawest thou, what does it
    mean?"
And when he answered not, but shook his head,
Clutching his heart as if in agony,
The patient Gurnemanz had patience then no
    more,
But thrust him out and quick made fast the
    door,
With the scant words: "Begone, thou guile-
    less lad!
Guileless thou mayst be; utter fool thou art!"
So Parsifal went forth into the world,
Naught knowing of the meaning of it all
Except the new-stirred pity in his heart.
And as the angry Gurnemanz returned,
And made his way along the pillared hall,
He stopped, amazed, and listened, for he heard
From far above a gentle voice that sang:
          "By pity 'lightened,
            My guileless One!"
And from the loftiest dome another voice:
            "Blessèd believing!"

29

PARSIFAL. PART II

THE TEMPTING OF PARSIFAL

KLINGSOR the dread magi-
cian plied his arts
And worked in shame his
dastardly black deeds,
Within the inner keep of a
great tower, —
The watch-tower of the grim
and frowning castle.
Here in a dark and dismal rocky room,
Where Heaven's light could scarcely find a way,
And where around him lay his books and tools
Of hateful magic, littering the floor,
Steadfast he looked upon a metal mirror
That told the fates to him, — then muttered low:
"The time has come! Lo, how my tower entices
The guileless lad, who cometh like a child
With happy heart, and laughter on his lips.
Come, I must work my work by her who sleeps
In heavy slumber underneath my spell;
For in the past she did my deadliest deeds."

And in the gloom he kindled incense rare,
That filled the keep with blue unearthly smoke;
And sitting at the mirror once again,
He called with mystic gestures to the depths
That yawned beneath an opening in the floor:
"Uprise! Come forth! Draw near me at my will!
Thy master calls thee, nameless wanderer,
Rose-bloom of Hell, and ancient devil-queen!
A thousand times the earth has known thy face
In many forms of woman's wiles and sins, —
Herodias wert thou in ancient time,
And once again Gundryggia wert called

33

In old Norse days; but thou art Kundry now,
Symbol of woman's wile and cruel craft.
Come hither, Kundry, for thy master calls!"

Then in the blue light Kundry slow appeared.
Asleep she seemed, and dreaming in her sleep,
But sudden wakened with a dreadful cry,
A shuddering cry, half laughter, half in pain.

And Klingsor spake again: "Awakest thou?
Again my spell is potent on thy life;
My will again shall use thee for my deeds."

But Kundry cried in bitter agony,
And wailed in fear and anguish at his feet;
While Klingsor asked her in deep thunder
    tones:
"Where hast thou wandered since I used thee
    last?
I know. Among the brethren of the Grail,
Who thought thee but a witch and serving-
    wench.
Do I not treat thee with a better grace,
And use thee for the mightiest of deeds?
Since thou didst lure for me the brave Am-
    fortas —
Chaste guardian (they thought him) of the
    Grail —
Thou hast deserted my high name and service.
What better hast thou found than me and
    mine?"

Then Kundry cried in hoarse and broken
    speech:
"O dismal night and shame and wickedness!

34

Would I could sleep the deepest sleep of
    death!"

And Klingsor asked: "What has there come
    to thee?
Has some one else awaked thee from thy sleep?"
And trembling Kundry answered: "Even so.
And, oh, the longing to redeem my life!"

Then Klingsor: "Yea, with knights so pure in
    heart,
The evil Kundry would be Heaven-pure."

But Kundry answered all his mockery:
"Yea, I did serve them well and faithfully."

And Klingsor spake with a great voice of
    scorn:
"Thou wouldst amend the mischief thou hast
    done? . . .
They are not worth it! They are fools and weak.
I buy them all for price of one sweet sin.
The strongest was the weakest in thine arms.
And so I ruined him, and won the Spear,
And left him with the ever-burning wound.
But now to-day another must be met,—
Most dangerous because so godlike pure,
For he is shielded by a guileless heart."

And Kundry cried: "Him will I never tempt!
Thou canst not force me to the hateful deed."
But Klingsor answered: "Yea, thou shalt, thou
    must.
I am thy master and I have the power.
Thy charms and woes are nothing unto me.

35

Laugh at me, if you will. I have the power!
Yea, I remember all the days of yore,—
That once I sought the holier, happier life,
Within the service of the Holy Grail;
But it was mad ambition, desperate wish,
And thou didst quench it for me, devil's-queen,
And drown it in thy hellish arts of love.
But that is past. Now thou art but my slave.
And Titurel, who scorned me at the gates,
And all his knights with their proud King Am-
fortas,
Through thy dark wiles I ruined utterly.
And in my hand I hold their sacred Spear
And soon shall have their shining Holy Grail.
Remember now to use thy wiles again
As thou didst love Amfortas to his shame."

But Kundry cried: "O misery and shame!
That e'en their King should be so weak with
me,
And all men weak. O hateful, hateful curse
That ruins them and me in sin together!
O for the sleep of death to end all this!"

And Klingsor then: "Perhaps thy wish is near,
For he who can defy thee, sets thee free.
Go tempt the guileless boy, and win thy wish."

But Kundry answered still: "I will not tempt
him!"

Then Klingsor: "Yea, thou must! It is my will.
For this I wakened thee. And fair is he.
See, from my window I can watch him come.

36

He scales the ramparts like a hero born.
This trumpet I will blow and wake the guards.
Ho! warders of the gates and walls! to arms!
A foe is near! . . . List to the clash of swords!
How my deluded vassals swarm the walls
To guard my castle and the maidens here —
Bewitching creatures fashioned by my art!
Behold! the guileless lad is not afraid!
He fights with bold Sir Ferris, wrests a sword,
And flashes it with fury in their midst."

And as he fought, Kundry laughed loud and
    long,
And now she groaned in awful agony,
Then with a sudden shriek was lost to sight.

Still Klingsor spake: "How ill his fiery zeal
Agrees with the weak spirit of these knights.
Wounded in arm and limb, they yield, they fly,
And carry off a multitude of scars.
But what care I, you puny, craven race?
Would that the weak knights of the Holy Grail
Might rise in wrath and slay each other thus!
How proudly stands the youth upon the walls!
How red the roses in his cheeks are laughing!
And how amazed he is, like some sweet child,
To see this wondrous garden at his feet!
Ho! Kundry! Hast thou gone? I thought I
    heard
Thy laughter, or a sudden cry of pain.
Doubtless already she is hard at work
To do my bidding, for she is my slave,
And what I tell her, she must surely do.
There, there, my gallant lad, so sweet and brave,

37

Thou art too young to understand these things.
But thou shalt learn, — my arts will teach thee
  well,
And when thy guileless heart shall be ensnared,
Then thou art weak, and lost, — and mine the
  Grail!"

Then, wondrous sight! the castle disappeared,
Save here and there a distant battlement,
And through the foliage the palace walls,
And windows of Arabian tracery.
But everywhere were flowers — wondrous
  flowers —
Rising in terraces of tropic growth:
A splendid garden of luxuriant flowers
Created by dread Klingsor's magic art.

And Parsifal, astounded at the scene,
Stood silently upon the castle walls,
As to his eye the great flowers seemed to wake,
And rush in airy garments here and there.
They seemed like maidens and they seemed
  like flowers,
So graceful and so beautiful were they.
And as they moved they spoke in rhythmic
  tones:

"HERE was the tumult and shoutings!
  Here was the clashing of weapons!

"Horror! our lovers are wounded!
  Here in the palace is carnage!

"Who is the foe that assails us?
  Accurst shall he be by us all!"

38

But Parsifal leaped gaily to their midst,
And smiled upon them with unfeigned delight;
And cried: "Thus do I win my way to you, —
The loveliest maidens that mine eyes have
    seen."

And pacified they ask: "Thou comest here
And wilt not harm us, but be kind to us?"

And Parsifal: "Nowhere such maidens live, —
Fair flowers of the garden of delight.
I could not treat you ill, you are so fair!
Again you bring sweet childhood's days to me,
For you are all so lovely and so bright."

And then the maidens welcomed the gay youth
And spake to him: "If thou wilt be our friend,
Then art thou welcome in our happy garden.
We do not play for gold, but only love, —
The rosebud garlands of the joy of life."

Then other maidens came in flowers clad,
And danced around him with their laughing
    grace,
And sang in tones of winsome witchery:

"WE are thy fragrant flowers,
    Blooming alone for thee,
And full of love's own bliss
And life's deep mystery!

"Come, kiss our rosy lips,
    For thou our lover art,
And taste the nectar sweet
Of nature's secret heart."

39

And Parsifal, still with the guileless heart,
And seeing all with only childlike eyes,
Untouched of evil, nor discerning sin,
Asked laughingly: "And are you really flowers?
I do not know. You are so beautiful."

Then crowded they around him with their
    charms,
And pleaded with him, "Love us ere we die!"
Crowded each other, jealous of his smile,
And struggling eagerly to win his love.

But Parsifal repulsed their too fond hearts,
And shunned their circle of entwining arms
With gentle gesture: "Sweetest sister-flowers,
I like ye better in the flowery dance,
And when ye give me space to see your
    charms.
Away, sweet sisters, leave me here alone!"

Then did they chide him: "Art afraid of us,
Or art thou also cold, as well as coward?
Here butterfly is wooed by loving flowers,
And does not know enough to sip the sweet."

And Parsifal discerned them then, and cried:
"Begone, false flowers, ye cannot snare my
    heart!"

But as he turned to leave the flowery throng,
He heard a sweet voice from a leafy bower
Say: "Parsifal! A moment! Parsifal!"

And quick he stopped and murmured, "Par-
    sifal!

40

Who calls me by that gentle mystic name,
That once my mother named me in her dreams?"

And the voice spake: "O tarry, Parsifal!
For I have joyous things to tell to thee.
Ye flowery children, leave him here in peace;
He came not here to waste his time in play.
Go to the wounded lovers waiting you."

And so they left him, singing as they went:

"MUST we leave thee, must we sever,
    Oh, the parting pain!
Gladly would we love thee ever
    And with thee remain!
Fair one, proud one, now farewell.
    Guileless, foolish heart, farewell!"

And gaily laughing at the guileless youth,
They rushed into the palace and were gone.
And Parsifal spake slowly to himself:
"Was all this nothing but a passing dream?"

But looking whence the other voice had come,
He saw the leafy bower had opened wide,
And on a flowery couch a maiden lay,
More beautiful than heart could ever dream,
Clad in some light gown of Arabian stuff.
And Parsifal, still standing high aloof,
Spake courteously: "Didst thou call to me
And name me who am nameless unto all?"

And she replied: "I named thee, guileless
    lad,—
I named thee by thine own name, Parsifal.

41

For so thy father Gamuret named thee,
Before he died in that Arabian land,—
Named thee before thine eyes had seen the light,
Named thee with greeting in his dying breath.
Here have I waited thee to tell thee all.
What drew thee here but the desire to know?"

And Parsifal: "I never saw, nor dreamed,
Such wondrous evil things as here to-day.
And art thou but another wanton flower
That bloomest in this evil garden here?"

But she: "O Parsifal, thou foolish heart!
Surely thou seest I am not as these.
My home lies far away in distant lands.
I did but tarry here to wait for thee
And tell thee many things about thyself.
I knew thee when thou wert a little babe,
Smiling upon thy loving mother's breast.
Thy earliest lisp still laugheth in my ear.
And thy dear widowed mother, sweet Hearts-
    rue,
Although she mourned, smiled also in her joy
When thou wert come, a laughing new-born
    love.
Thy cradle was a nest of softest moss,
And her caresses lulled thee to thy sleep.
She watched thee lovingly through all thy sleep
And waked thee in the morning with her tears
Of mingled love and pain for him who died.
And that thy life should know no strife of men,
Nor care nor perils as thy sire had known,
Became her only care. So in the woods
She went with thee to hide in quiet there.

42

And there she hoped no evil of the world,
Nor ways of sinful men would come to thee.
Didst thou not hear her sorrowful lament
When thou didst roam too far or late from home?
Didst thou not hear her laughter in her joy
When she would give thee welcome home
  again, —
When her dear arms were close around thy
  neck
And her sweet kisses on thy loving lips?
But thou hast never known what I have known
Of those last days of thy dear mother's love.
Thou didst not hear the secret sighs and moans,
And at the last the tempest of her grief,
When after many days thou didst not come,
And not a trace of thee could e'er be found.
She waited through the weary days and nights,
And then her open tears and cries were stilled,
And secret grief was eating at her life,
Until at last her anguished heart did break,
And thy dear mother, gentle Heartsrue, died."

And Parsifal in tenderest grief drew near,
And sank in sorrow at the maiden's feet,
And cried: "O woe is me! What have I done,
O sweetest, dearest, gentlest mother mine,
That I thy son shouldst bring thee to thy death?
O blind I was, and wretched, and accurst
To wander off and leave thy tender love.
O faithful, fondest, fairest of all mothers!"

And Parsifal was weak with pain and grief,
And gently did the maiden bend to him
And wreathe her arms confiding round his neck.

43

And whisper to him: "Since thou knowest grief,
Let me be comfort to thy sorrowing heart.
And let thy bitter woe find sweet relief
In consolations of the tenderest love."

But Parsifal: "Yea, yea, I did forget
The mother that hath borne me in her love.
And how much else have I forgotten now!
What have I yet remembered to my good?
A blindness seems to hold me in its thrall."

Then said the maiden: "Thou hast spoken true,
But full confession endeth sorrow's pain,
And sadness brings its fuller gift of wisdom.
Thy heart has learned its lesson of deep grief;
Now it should learn its lesson of sweet love,
Such love as burned in thine own father's heart
Whene'er he held dear Heartsrue to his breast.
Thy mother with her flaming heart of love
Gave thee her life, — it throbs within thee now, —
And thus she sends her blessing from above,
And gives to thee this sweetest kiss of love."

And at the words she held him in her arms,
And pressed upon his lips a fervent kiss.

Then there was silence, deep and terrible,
As if the destiny of all the world
Hung in the balance of that fervent kiss.
But still she held him in her clinging arms. . . .
Then Parsifal, as if the kiss had stung
His being into horror of new pain,

Sprang up with anguish in his pallid face, —
His hands held tight against his throbbing
    heart,
As if to stifle some great agony, —
And at the last he cried with voice of pain:
"Amfortas! O Amfortas! O Amfortas!
I know it now! The Spear-wound in thy side!
It burns my heart! It sears my very soul!
O grief and horror in my being's depth!
O misery! O anguish beyond words!
The wound is bleeding here in mine own side!"

And as the maiden watched him in her fear,
He spake again in fierce and awful strain:
"Nay, this is not the Spear-wound in my side!
There let the life-blood flow itself to death!
For this is fire and flame within my heart
That sways my senses in delirium, —
The awful madness of tormenting love!
Now do I see how all the world is stirred,
Tossed and convulsed, and often lost in shame
By the terrific passions of the heart!"

Then growing calmer, Parsifal spake on,
As if an echo of the wail of God
Over the world's sad suffering and sin:
"I seem to see the blessed Holy Cup
And in its depths the Saviour's blood doth glow.
The rapture of redemption sweet and mild
Trembleth afar through all the universe,
Except within a sin-polluted heart.
Such is Amfortas whom I must redeem.
I heard the suffering Saviour's sad lament
Over His sanctuary shamed in sin;

45

I heard His words — 'Deliver me from hands
That have profaned the holiest with guilt!'
So rang the words within my very soul.
Yet I, forgetting what my Lord had said,
Have wandered off in boyish foolishness. . . .
O Lord, behold my sorrow at Thy feet!
Have mercy on me, blest Redeemer mine,
And show me how my sin can be atoned!"

Then came the maiden near in trembling way,
As if her wonder was to pity turned,
And spake: "My noble knight, fling off this
    spell!
Look up, and this heart's love shall comfort
    thee!"
But Parsifal with fixed look answered her:
"Ah, woman, now I know thee who thou art.
Thy voice it was that pleaded with Amfortas;
Thine eye that smiled away his peace of heart;
Thy lips that tempted him to taste of sin;
This same white throat was bending over him;
This proudly tossing head; these laughing
    curls;
So these fair arms were winding round his neck;
And every feature soft in flattery;
When thou didst bring him agony untold,
And stole his soul's salvation with thy kiss!
Out and away, destroyer of men's souls!
Take thy pernicious wiles and get thee gone!"

But Kundry — for 't was she — cried out in grief:
"O heart, that feelest for Amfortas' woe,
Hast thou no feeling for my dire distress?
Thou camest here to save the King from sin,

46

Why not save me and bring me my redemption?
Through endless ages I have waited thee, —
For thou dost seem to me a very savior,
Like Him whom long ago I did revile.
O that thou knewest my story and the curse
Which waking, sleeping, joyous, or in woe,
Brings me forth sorrow and a deep despair.
This is my story. Once I saw the Lord
In those sad days of His sad earthly life,
For in a previous existence I
Was also living in fair Galilee;
These eyes did see Him on the dolorous way
That led His sorrowing feet to Calvary.
And in light scorn, I laughed at Him. . . . I
    laughed."

And when she spake these words — "I
    laughed" —
She stopped in pain and for an awful moment
Her deed spake in the silence, horror-stricken.
And Parsifal deep shuddered at the word,
But she spake on: "I laughed at Him. Whereat
He looked at me. Ah! ne'er shall I forget! . . .
And now forever am I seeking Him,
From age to age and e'en from world to world,
To stand once more before Him in contrition.
Sometimes His eye doth seem to glance on me,
And then accursèd laughter seizes me,
And I am ready for the deeds of Hell.
I laugh and laugh, but never can I weep.
I wander storming, raving, but no tears.
The night of madness holds me, but no tears.
O could I weep, I know I would be saved.
Be pitiful, and be a savior to me!

47

For thee, like Him, I have derided oft.
Now do I come to thee with heart of love;
Let me but rest upon thy breast and weep.
Take me but to thyself for one short hour,
And thou shalt save eternity for me,
And in my tears my sin shall be atoned!"

But Parsifal: "Eternity were lost
For both of us, if even for an hour
I yielded to the sin of loving thee,
And in that hour forgot my holy mission.
For I am also sent to save thy soul
And to deliver thee from curse of lust.
The love that burns in thee is only lust.
Between that and the pure love of true hearts
There yawns abyss like that 'twixt Heaven and
    Hell;
Nor can the foul fount e'er be closed in thee,
Until the pure fount shall be opened wide;
Nor can thy sinful heart be ever saved
By heavy sorrow and much agony;
Nor e'en by service rendered unto others;
Only one way can save thy guilty soul —
Only by giving all to Christ's dear love.
The curse that rests upon the brotherhood
Is something different by another's sin.
They pine and languish for the Holy Grail,
And yet they know the wondrous fount of life.
But thou! what wouldst thou do to save thy
    soul?
O misery! O false and daring deed!
Thou wouldst see rest and Heaven's holy peace,
By way of Hell, and death's eternal night!"

Then Kundry cried in wildest ecstasy:

48

"And hath a single kiss from me conveyed
Such boundless knowledge to thine eager soul,
And given unto thee a world-wide vision?
O let my perfect love embrace thy heart,
And it shall quicken thee to godlike power!
Deliver sin-lost souls! It is thy work!
Stand as a god revealed! It is thy right!
Take thou my love, and take this godlike power,
And let me perish! Thou art all to me!"

Then Parsifal: "I offer thee deliverance,
But not in this way, impious one."

But Kundry: "Let me love thee, my divine one!
This the deliverance I ask of thee."

And Parsifal: "Love and deliverance
Shall come to thee in truest, noblest way,
If thou wilt guide me to Amfortas now."

Then Kundry into maddened fury broke,
And cried: "No, never shalt thou find the King.
Let the doomed King go to his desperate
    shame.
Ah! hapless wretch whom I derided laughing,
He fell at last by his own sacred Spear."

Then Parsifal: "The King was brave and good.
Who dared to wound him with the sacred
    Spear?"

And Kundry answered: "He has wounded him!
He who can put my laughter into flight!
He who enslaves me to his utter will!
His spell is on me and doth give me might.

49

Yea, and the Spear shall also thrust thee
    through,
If thou wilt pity that poor craven's fate!
O Parsifal, pray give to me thy pity!
Let but one single hour be mine and thine,
And then thou shalt be guided as thou wilt!"

And as she spake, she sought to hold him fast,
But off he thrust her with the last fierce words:
"Unhand me, wretched woman! Be ye gone!"

And Kundry beat her breast and cried in rage:
"Hither, ye powers of darkness! Hither, help!
Seize on the caitiff who defies my will!
Guard ye the ways, and ward the passage there!
Ah, Parsifal, if thou shouldst fly from hence
And learn the ways through all the weary world,
The one Way that thou seekest to the King—
That thou shalt never find! So have I sworn!
So do I curse all pathways and all courses
That lead thee from me. Wander, then, I say!
Wander forever, but the King find never!
I give thee up to Klingsor as thy guide, —
Klingsor my royal Lord and magic Master."

And scarce the words had left her cursing lips,
Than Klingsor's ugly form was on the wall.
In his black hands he swung the sacred Spear
And cried: "Halt there, thou cursèd guileless
    One!
Feel thou the keenness of thy Master's Spear!"

With that, he hurled it full at Parsifal;
But miracle of miracles! it stopped
Above the head of Parsifal, and there

It floated in the radiant air, a glory.
And Parsifal, with upward look and prayer,
Grasped it and wielded with supremest joy,
And with it marked upon the air, the cross;

And cried: "This sign of holy cross I make,
And ban thy cursèd magic evermore.
And as it soon shall heal the burning wound,
So may it wound thy power to utter wreck!"

And as the words of Parsifal were said,
An earthquake shook the castle to the ground,
The garden withered into desert waste
Strewn with the flowers, faded, desolate, —
And Kundry, crying loud, fell to the earth.

So Parsifal held high the holy Spear
And left the garden-waste and broken tower,
And all the ruin of the haunts of sin,
But stood a moment on the shattered walls
And looked at Kundry lying on the ground,
And spake: "Thou knowest where we meet
    again!"
And as he went, sad Kundry raised herself
A little, and looked after him.

                        O Kundry!
Sinful and yet desiring to be helped,
Enthralled of sin, yet seeking after God!
Thou art our human nature, after all, —
Strange contradiction, mingled love and hate,
Half demon and half angel in thy moods!

51

PARSIFAL. PART III.

THE CROWNING OF PARSIFAL

MORNING was breaking in
the pleasant land,
Where rising meadows full
of fragrant flowers
Skirt with their beauty the
deep forest wilds,
That lead to rocky cliffs
among whose peaks
Lies Monsalvat, the castle of the Grail.

Forth from a hut that leans against the rock,
Close to a woodland spring, came Gurnemanz,
The faithful knight and noble counsellor,
But now a lonely hermit of the woods,
Clad in the sacred tunic of the Grail,
Grown very old and bent, and hair snow-white.

He listened for awhile, then spake: "What
moans
From yonder thicket come? No forest beast
Doth utter cry so piteous and sad.
This holy morn, the holiest of the year,
Doth bring to Nature a deep-thrilling joy.
'T is only humankind that can be sad.
Ah! there again the grieving and the moans,—
Methinks I know that sad despairing cry.
These brambles I will tear apart and see
What their thick undergrowth so well con-
ceals.
Ah! Here she is again! The winter's thorn
Has been her grave these many weary years.
Wake, Kundry, wake! The winter long is past;
The spring has come! Awaken with the flowers!

How cold she is, and rigid as the dead!
I could believe her dead, — and yet I heard
Her groaning and her piteous moan erstwhile."

And kneeling down, he chafed her hands and
    face,
Breathed on them to awaken life again;
And at the last a tremor thrilled her through.
In deep amaze she wakened from her sleep,
And opened her sad eyes, with startled cries.
Long did she gaze on agèd Gurnemanz;
Then she arose, but her whole mien was
    changed, —
The wildness of her former life was gone;
A tender softness shone forth from her eyes;
A gentle bearing lent an added grace;
And without word of question, or of thanks,
Away she moved as if a serving-maid.

Then Gurnemanz: "Hast thou no word for me?
Are these my thanks, that from the sleep of
    death
I waked thee?"
                    Kundry slowly bent her head,
And murmured brokenly the words: "To
    serve, —
O let me serve thee and the Holy Grail."

Then Gurnemanz again: "This were light
    toil, —
For days of saddest peace have come to us,
And deeds of valiant arms no more are done.
A dark despair is over Monsalvat;
No messengers are sent to distant parts
To stir the hearts of fighting warriors;

56

Like every creature of the leafy woods,
Each man doth serve himself in daily needs."
But Kundry had perceived the hermit-hut,
And knew that she could serve in little things;
And unto it she went to find some task.

And Gurnemanz deep wondered, and he spoke:
"How unlike days of yore her step and way,—
Grace in her step and grace in countenance.
Perchance God giveth grace to her sad heart.
Perchance this holy morn hath wrought the
    change.
O day of boundless mercy, 't was for this—
Her soul's salvation and another life—
That I have wakened her from sleep of death!
See, with a pitcher comes she from the hut,
And fills it at the spring! . . . But who is this
That now I see approaching through the
    woods
And drawing slowly near the holy spring?
Yon knight is not a brother of the Grail,
With all that war accoutrement of gloom."

And one drew near, a splendid armored knight,
His armor shining black as darkest night,
His helmet closed, and lowered was his spear.
Forward he walked as if he moved in dream,
As if a servant of some high emprise,
Neither to right nor left he turned his face,
But seated him beyond the holy spring.

And Gurnemanz close watched him and his
    ways
And wondered who the splendid knight might
    be;

57

Then ventured near with courteous salute:
"All hail to thee, sir knight, and welcome here!
Art thou astray, and may I give thee aid? . . .
No word for me, but bowing of thy head?
Perchance my lord is under knightly vow
To perfect silence, as my vows bind me
To courtesy and service. Therefore hear
Where now thou art and what is due this place.
This is a holy woods and this a holy spring,
Within the domain of the Holy Grail,
Where in his armor none hath right to come
With helmet closed, and shield and shining
    spear.
Besides, dost thou not know what day this is?
Not know the day? From whence then hast
    thou come?
What heathen darkness hath been thine abode
That thou rememberest not this holy day,—
The ever-hallowèd Good-Friday morn?
Put off thy heavy armor, for the Lord,
Bare of defence, on this most holy day,
Did freely shed His blood to save the world,
And bring the time of kindness and of peace."

And silently, without an answering word,
The stranger knight fixed in the ground his
    spear,
And at its foot lay down his shield and sword,
Opened his helmet, placed it on the ground,
And knelt in silent prayer before the spear.

With wonder and deep feeling, Gurnemanz
Had watched the knight, and as he saw him
    pray

58

And saw the face upturnèd to the light,
He knew him, and to Kundry softly spake,
Who now drew near: "Thou knowest him.
 'T is he
Who long ago laid low the snow-white swan, —
He whom in anger I thrust out-of-doors.
Where has he wandered since that luckless
 day?
But look! Behold the spear! It is the Spear
For which my eager heart has longed and
 prayed!
O holy day, on which the Spear comes home!
O happy day to which my soul awakes!"

And when the knight had ended all his prayer,
He slowly rose, and looked about and saw
The agèd hermit, snowy-crowned with age;
And suddenly he knew that kindly form,
And rushed to Gurnemanz with eager face,
And crying: "Good my friend, all hail to thee!
Thank Heaven that I find thee once again!"

And Gurnemanz: "Dost thou remember me,
After so many long and weary years,
And bent with grief and care as now I am,
And covered with the clustering snow of age?
But tell me, what has passed since last we met?
And how didst thou come here, and whence,
 and why?"

And Parsifal — for it was he — replied:
"Through error and through sufferings I come,
Through many failures and through countless
 woes.
Thus was the guileless One at last enlightened,

59

And taught the depths of pity and of love.
And can it be that now the trials are ended
And peace has come, and holiness at last?
Yet here I am within this holy wood,
And here art thou, dear servant of the Grail.
But, do I err, this place seems somehow
    changed
From what it was in days of yore? The life,
The joy seem to have vanished, and I feel
As if a cloud hung over Monsalvat."

Then Gurnemanz: "Too true thine every word,
But tell me, pray, for whom thou here dost
    seek?"

And with a wondrous light within his eyes,
Did Parsifal with earnest words reply:
"I come to him whose piteous moans of pain
I heard long years ago, nor understood. —
The guileless One went forth from thee a boy,
Impetuous, fierce, who did not know himself;
He comes again a man with tenderest pity,
And deep experience and heart enlightened,
To be the healer of the stricken King.
But long the course by which I learned the way,
And bitter all the wanderings, where sin
Had laid its snares, and sought to curse my
    soul.
Many the perils and right fierce the strife,
Yet clung I to the pathway of the right.
And at the last I won the sacred Spear
By God's good mercy and His boundless love.
But even with the Spear within my hands
Oft came a fearful dread upon my heart,

60

Lest I might lose this treasure that He gave
Into my keeping, for never durst I use
This sacred Spear in battle-blows or strife, —
It was for healing wounds, not making them, —
And so in many a fight I took the wounds
From other weapons, but profaned this never.
I bring it home virgin and undefiled,
And consecrate it to its healing work.
Thus does it gleam before thee, even now, —
The wonder-working power, the sacred
  Spear!"

And Gurnemanz, with joyous heart, replied:
"O grace and glory, blessèd gift of God!
O miracle of holy healing power
That thou hast brought us in the sacred Spear!
Sir knight, if it were once a cruel thing
That drove thee wandering in the evil world,
And if it ever were a curse to strive
In subtle snares and temptings manifold,
Believe me, now the spell is surely broken.
Here thou art now within the Grail's dominion.
Here wait for thee an eager band of knights.
Ah! how they need the blessing that thou
  bringest.
For since that morning when thou first wert
  here,
The sorrow and the anguish that thou heard'st
Have grown until the woe has covered all.
And King Amfortas, soul and body wracked,
Did crave in desperation only death,
And so refused to show the Holy Grail.
No prayer, no sorrow of his brother-knights
Could move him to fulfil his sacred trust.

61

Close in its shrouded shrine the Cup remained.
For King Amfortas hopes that if his eyes
Shall see the Grail no more, that he may die,
And with his life thus end his bitter pain.
The holy Supper also is denied us, —
Our daily portion only common food.
Thereby exhausted is our former strength.
No more the cry for succor comes to us,
Nor call to holy war from distant lands;
But pale and wretched wander forth the
    knights,
Hopeless and leaderless in these dark days.
Here in the forest I myself have hid,
In quiet waiting for the hour of death,
Already come unto my warrior-lord,
The aged Titurel. For when no more
He could behold the vision of the Grail,
Then did his sad heart fail him, and he died."

And Parsifal in sudden sorrow cried:
"What have I done to let this curse go on?
Why have I wasted all these precious years
In wandering, while here was deepest woe?
Why did I never see the needed truth
That no repentance can assuage the grief,
No expiation can atone the wrong,
Until another feels the bitter pain,
And takes it willingly to his own heart?
Here I was chosen to redeem the wrong,
And save the anguish of the stricken King,
And yet how blind has been my foolish heart!
Can blindness mean impurity and sin,
And may it be that I am all deceived, —
My way all lost, my hopes forever gone?"

And in the bitter struggle of his soul,
And in the self-abasement of his heart,
And in the strong reaction that oft comes
To spiritual natures, deep and fine,
He would have fallen helpless to the ground;
But Gurnemanz quick caught him in his arms,
And led him sinking to a grassy mound,
And Kundry ran with water for his brow.

But Gurnemanz: "Not so. The holy spring
Shall now revive our pilgrim's waning strength.
My heart sees noble work for him to-day.
A sacred mystic duty doth await him.
He shall be pure as light, and all the dust
Of travel and of error washed away!"

Then from his limbs they took the mighty
        greaves,
And loosed the woven corselet from his side,
And bathed his feet and brought him to himself.

And straight he asked: "And shall I see the
        King?"

And Gurnemanz: "Thou shalt behold the King
This very day and speak thy word to him.
The death-rites of mine agèd warrior-lord,
The noble Titurel, doth call me to the court;
And there again the Grail shall be revealed.
For King Amfortas hath by solemn vow
Promised once more to open up the shrine,
Sworn to fulfil the long-neglected office,
To sanctify the saintly father's end,
And expiate the deep unfilial crime,
The added sin, that broke his father's heart."

And as he spoke, the kindly Kundry bathed
The feet of Parsifal, who looked at her
With gentle wonder and a pitying love,
And said: "So humbly hast thou washed my
feet,
Perchance the good and faithful Gurnemanz
May sprinkle my poor head with holy water,
And give my soul his gracious benediction."

And Gurnemanz took water from the spring,
And sprinkled Parsifal in holy rite,
And uttered over him the benediction:
"O guileless One, thrice blessed be and pure,
And free forever from all care and sin!"

Then Kundry from her bosom drew a vial,
A golden vial, full of perfumed oil,
And poured its soothing fragrance on his feet
And dried them with her flowing unbound hair.

And Parsifal reached out and took the vial,
And gave it unto Gurnemanz and said:
"This woman hath anointed these my feet;
Let now the faithful servant of the Grail,
And minister of sainted Titurel,
Anoint my chosen head with holy oil,
That I may take the office, as God will,
And you to-day may greet me as your King."

So Gurnemanz performed the kingly rite,
Anointing Parsifal with holy oil,
And laid the hands of blessing on his head,
And said: "So came the ancient word to us;
So with my blessing do I greet thee now,

And hail thee as the God-elected King!
Thou art His guileless One, by pity 'lightened,
Patient in suffering, and taught by woe.
Much hast thou suffered to redeem another;
God give thee now the grace for crowning all."

Then Parsifal took water from the spring,
And came to Kundry kneeling at his feet,
And sprinkled her with solemn mystic rite,
And said: "This be the first work of my trust.
Kundry, in Christ's dear name I sprinkle thee.
Be thou redeemed and holy evermore!"

And in a passion of rejoicing tears
She kneeled there and her voice gave praise
    to God.

And Parsifal looked on the fields and woods,
So fair and radiant in the morning light,
And uttered forth the rapture of his heart:
"How beautiful these morning meadows are!
So fresh, so sweet, so radiantly pure!
Full many a flower in other days I saw,
But full of subtle poison was their breath
And they were snares of baneful witchery.
But these are God's own blossoms full of grace.
These twining vines that burst with purple
    bloom,
These fragrant flowers, so innocent and fair,—
They speak to me of loving childhood's days,
And tell me of the boundless love of God."

Then Gurnemanz: "On fair Good-Friday morn,
All nature seems a-thrill with new delight."

65

And Parsifal: "Yet strange that it is so.
That darkest day of agony divine
Might well have cast a pall of gloom o'er all,
And plunged all Nature into deepest woe."

"No, no," the gentle Gurnemanz replied,
"The Saviour's work hath wrought a miracle,
And now the grateful tears of penitence
Are holy dew that falls upon the world,
And makes it bloom in fair and lustrous beauty;
And all creation knows God's saving work,
And praises Him for His redeeming grace.
No more the agony of that grim Cross,
But now the joy of man redeemed and saved,
Freed from the load of sin by conquering faith,
And purified by Love's great sacrifice.
Each sprouting blade and meadow-flower doth
    see
Something of God's grace in the heart of man;
For as the Lord was tender unto man,
So man in turn will love God's flowering earth.
The whole creation therefore doth rejoice,
And every bird and flower is full of praise,
And Nature everywhere is full of God,
And sweet has dawned this day of innocence."

Then Kundry, with the tears still in her eyes,
Looked up at Parsifal, and soft he spake:
"I saw the hearts that mocked us fade away,
But love shall bloom eternal in God's grace.
Blest tears that speak the blessing in thy heart.
But weep no more. God's grace is full of joy, —
Smile with all Nature, joyously redeemed!"

66

And down he bent, and on her pure white brow
Printed the kiss of God's redeeming love.

Then chimed the distant bells, and louder yet
The gradual growing music of sweet sounds.

And Gurnemanz: "The hour has come, midday.
Permit me now to lead thee to the Grail!"

And Parsifal was clothed in holy garb, —
The dove-embroidered mantle of the Grail, —
Which Gurnemanz had brought him from the
    hut,
And grasped the sacred Spear and followed on.

Again they climbed the rocky passages,
And reached at last the castle's pillared hall,
Crowned with the mighty dome of blazing
    light.
Slowly the knights in mourning garb marched
    in,
Bearing the corpse of saintly Titurel.
Slowly the servitors marched sadly in,
Bearing the pale Amfortas on his couch.
And going on in front the acolytes
Bore in the Grail in heavy covered shrine.
And as they marched, they sang this solemn
    hymn:

"HERE do we bear the Holy Grail,
        Long hidden in this shrine;
No more its wondrous grace is seen,
    No more its glories shine!

"Here saintly Titurel we bear,
    The faithful knight and king;

67

When he no more the Grail could see,
  He died in sorrowing!

"And here Amfortas now we bear—
  God shrive him from the past;
For he has sworn to do his trust
  And show the Grail at last!"

And suffering Amfortas turned and groaned,
And raised himself a little on his couch,
And cried: "O woe is me! O woe is me!
My tears are flowing from my very heart.
Would I had died before I saw this hour.
Yet death is mercy that I cannot hope."

Then solemnly the knights, with sacred awe,
Uncovered saintly Titurel, and looked
Once more upon that well-belovèd face,
And there was sound of weeping everywhere.
And sadly did Amfortas speak the words:
"My father, blest among God's heroes ever!
Thou before whom the angels loved to bow,
Forgive me for my most unfilial sin,—
I sought for death, yet struck thee to the heart,
By holding back the vision of the Grail.
O thou who now in radiance divine
Dost see the blest Redeemer face to face,
Beseech for me that when I show the Grail
It may give life anew to these dear knights—
But death to me—sweet death for which I long.
O death, kind mercy of the living God,
Stifle this heart and rid me of my pain!
Father, I plead with thee to cry to Him:
'Redeemer, give my son release and peace!'"

68

Thereat the knights came pressing up and
    cried:
"Unveil the Grail and do thine office now!
The death-rite of thy father doth demand it!"

But in a mad despair Amfortas rose,
And wildly rushed among the startled knights,
And cried: "No, no, I cannot do it now!
Death is so near me, only let me die!
Why should I turn again to dreadful life?
Rather I plead with you to slay me here!
See, here I stand, the open wound is here!
Thus am I poisoned, here flows forth the blood!
Draw ye your swords and plunge them to the
    hilt!
Kill both the sinner and his awful pain!
Then will the Grail forever shine for you,
And blessing come to you for evermore!"

But all shrank back in terror from the King,
Who stood in frenzied madness there alone.

Then Parsifal drew near, and slowly spake:
"Only one weapon serves to kill that pain.
The one that struck can staunch thy wound
    again!"

And with the sacred Spear he touched the King.
And lo! a miracle of healing power! —
The wound was staunched and a deep thrill of
    love
Changed agony to rapture all divine.

And Parsifal spake on: "Thou art forgiven.
Body and soul are cleansed by God's free grace.

69

Thy life for evermore shall happy be
Within the service of the Holy Grail.
But never more as King, for I have come
To take thy place as God hath so decreed.
Thy sorrows shall be blessings unto thee,
For thus by pity was the guileless 'lightened,
And God's own Son was perfect made by pain.
Knights of the Grail, behold the sacred Spear!
God gave it me but to restore to you!"

And all with reverent joy beheld the Spear,
And thanked the Lord that it had come again
To bring the golden days of health and power.
And as they looked in rapture and in awe,
The Spear-point seemed to glow with holy
  fire
And sparkled, turning red like flowing blood.

And Parsifal spoke on: "O miracle
And marvel of the holy power of God.
This sacred Spear is flowing with the blood,
The very blood of that same wondrous Saviour,
That floweth in the crystal of the Grail.
The double blessing shall its glory give.
Open the shrine! Reveal the Holy Grail!"

And quick the sacred shrine was opened wide
And Parsifal long knelt in silent prayer,
Absorbed in holy rapture at the sight.

Then suddenly the heavenly splendor fell
And flamed and glowed within the sacred Cup,
While wondrous glory flooded all the hall
And filled each heart with deep and holy joy.

And from the lofty dome a dove descended,
And hovered lovingly o'er Parsifal.

Thus Parsifal was crowned of God and man,
And slowly did he lift the Holy Grail,
The red blood glowing with its wondrous light,
And waved it in the air before the knights,
Who knelt around him, praising God on high.
And there had Kundry come with new-found
    faith
And crept within the splendor of the Grail
And, with its light upon her, died, — redeemed!

And still did Parsifal hold up the Grail,
Seeming a vision of the very Christ,
His crimson mantle changed to lustrous white-
    ness.
His lips seemed speaking loving benediction;
And marvellous the red glow of the Grail;
And beautiful the white dove soaring there.
While from the heights the softest voices sang:

    "Highest wonder! blest salvation!
        Praise the Lord for our redemption!"

THE END

And from the lofty dome a dove descended,
And hovered lovingly o'er Parsifal.

Thus Parsifal was crowned of God and man,
And slowly did he lift the Holy Grail.
The red blood glowing with its wondrous light,
And waved it in the air before the Knights,
Who knelt around him, praising God on high,
And there had Kundry come with new-found faith
And crept within the splendor of the Grail
And, with its light upon her, died, — redeemed!

And still did Parsifal hold up the Grail,
Seeming a vision of the very Christ,
His crimson mantle changed to lustrous whiteness.
His lips seemed speaking loving benediction;
And marvellous the red glow of the Grail,
And beautiful the white dove soaring there.
While from the heights the softest voices sang:

"Highest wonder! bless't salvation!
Praise the Lord for our redemption!"

THE END